My First Stories from
the Ramayan

My First Stories from the Ramayan

ISBN: 978-93-5049-437-0

Printed in 2016

© Shree Book Centre

Retold by
Sunita Pant Bansal

Published by

Shree Book Centre

8, Kakad Industrial Estate, S. Keer Marg, off L. J. Road
Matunga (west), Mumbai 400 016, India
Tel.: +91-22-2437 7516 / 2437 4559 / 2438 0907
Fax: +91-22-2430 9183
Email: sales@shreebookcentre.com
Website: **www.shreebookcentre.com**

Contents

Preface

The Ramayan is one of the two great epics of India. Written by the Sanskrit poet Valmiki, the original Ramayan is believed to be a long epic poem with 24,000 couplets.

One of the world's most widely-read classics, the Ramayan narrates the life of Prince Ram. It contains many morals that teach us how to live in various situations.

Ram lived his entire life by the rules of *dharma*. He was considered an ideal son, brother, husband and ruler. This epic teaches children the importance of devotion, duty and relationships, as well as the truth that good always wins over evil, no matter what.

My First Stories from the Ramayan is a collection of twelve carefully picked moral tales from the epic, which are inspiring and valuable for children. The volume is targeted at the early readers of the Ramayan, aged six and above.

The stories are written in simple language, accompanied by colourful illustrations. The dialogue bubbles help understand what the characters think and feel. The glossary of difficult words at the end of the book will enrich children's vocabulary.

Happy reading.

The Princes of Ayodhya

Long ago, in what we now call Uttar Pradesh, there was the kingdom of Kosal. It was a very rich kingdom, and the people there were very happy. The capital of Kosal was the magnificent and beautiful city of Ayodhya. It was situated on the banks of the

River Sarayu. No enemy could ever conquer this city; hence it was called Ayodhya, which means 'unconquerable'.

Kosal was ruled for hundreds of years by the great kings of the Ikshvaku dynasty. The kings believed that their ancestors were the children of the sun god Surya.

Dashrath was one of the many kings who had ruled Ayodhya. He was a brave and kind king. He fought many battles against the evil kings. He protected his people and helped the needy. So the people of Ayodhya loved him. He should have been happy, but he was not. He had no children. This made the king very sad. He was growing old and was afraid

that he would die without a child. His three wives, Kausalya, Kaikeyi and Sumitra, also wished to have children.

One day, the family priest, Sage Vashishth, advised Dashrath to perform a *yajna*, a special prayer. "This *yajna* will make the gods happy and they will bless you with a son," he said. The king agreed to the suggestion.

The priests made arrangements for the *yajna* on the banks of the River Sarayu. The *yajna* began. At the end of the ceremony, Agnidev, the God of Fire, appeared before them. He had a silver bowl in his hands. He said, "Dashrath, take this *prasad* and give it

Dashrath, give this to your queens and your wish will be fulfilled.

Kausalya, divide this *prasad* among the queens.

to your wives. You will soon have children."
He gave the king the bowl and disappeared.

The happy king quickly went to the palace and gave the bowl to his first wife, Kausalya. He said, "All my wives should eat this *prasad*." Kausalya gave half of it to Kaikeyi. Both Kausalya and Kaikeyi then gave half their share to Sumitra.

The three queens ate the *prasad* eagerly. Soon they were blessed with lovely sons. Kausalya's son was born first and he was named Ram. Kaikeyi's son Bharat was born next. Since Sumitra ate two portions of the *prasad*, she gave birth to twins. They were called Lakshman and Shatrughan.

The king was very happy. The whole of Ayodhya rejoiced the birth of the princes for many days.

When the princes turned five, they were ready for school. In those days, children were sent to a *gurukul* in the nearby forest to study. The children lived with their guru and learnt all that they could from him. The four princes of Ayodhya were also sent to a *gurukul*.

Sage Vashishth was their guru. He taught them well. Ram, Lakshman, Bharat and Shatrughan learnt the Vedas and the Shastras. They were trained to be warriors, using the bow and arrow and other weapons.

After some years, the princes completed their education at the *gurukul.* They returned to their palace in Ayodhya. Everyone was delighted to see the well-mannered and brave boys.

Their mothers especially were very happy that their sons were back home. They pampered the boys for many days with their favourite *laddoos* and other sweets and snacks.

Everyone in Ayodhya noticed that Ram and Lakshman were inseparable. Bharat and Shatrughan loved to go hunting and play together.

Whenever the princes played a friendly game, Ram and Lakshman always paired up; Bharat and Shatrughan were the other team. All four brothers loved each other a lot.

Vishwamitra's Request

Now that the princes were grown up, Dashrath wanted to get them married. One day, he was in his court discussing this matter with the priests and the ministers. Suddenly, a guard rushed in and announced, "The great Sage Vishwamitra has come to Ayodhya!"

The king, the ministers and the royal priests rushed out to meet Sage Vishwamitra, one of the greatest sages of India. Dashrath welcomed the sage to his palace. He said, "Great Vishwamitra, the people of Ayodhya are blessed by your visit." Vishwamitra smiled and said "Dashrath, I have come here to ask you a favour."

Dashrath replied, "It will be my pleasure to serve you. What can I do for you?"

Vishwamitra said, "I am performing a *yajna* at my ashram. It has been some time since we started the *yajna*, but we are finding it difficult to complete it." Dashrath and his ministers were puzzled. Vishwamitra

was after all a powerful sage. What could be stopping him from completing his *yajna*?

Vishwamitra continued, "The demons led by Mareech and Suvahu have been troubling us. They make the *yajna* impure by throwing flesh and blood into the fire, and we have to start the whole ritual again. I can kill them with a curse, but according to the rules of the *yajna*, I cannot use my powers to curse anyone during the *yajna*."

Dashrath was listening intently. Even before he could say anything, Vishwamitra said, "I want you to send your son Ram with me immediately. I will be able to complete the *yajna* with Ram's help."

Dashrath hesitated. Ram had just returned from the *gurukul*. He was too young and did not have enough experience. So the king said, "Sage Vishwamitra, I will send my entire army with you instead of Ram."

Vishwamitra said, "Remember, you promised to give me whatever I wanted. Trust me when I say that Ram is the only one who can put an end to my problem."

Sage Vashishth advised Dashrath, "Do not worry, King! Send Ram and Lakshman with Vishwamitra. His strengths are great, his knowledge is vast, and he can see the past as

well as the future. We need not worry about the princes as long as they are with him."

Finally, Dashrath agreed to send Ram and Lakshman with Vishwamitra. The three of them travelled down the River Sarayu and reached the place where Sarayu met the River Ganga.

A little later, they crossed the Ganga and walked to Siddhashram where Vishwamitra and his followers were performing the *yajna*.

Ram and Lakshman stood guard while the sages performed the *yajna*. Soon they saw two demons flying towards the ashram.

Ram's powerful arrow threw Mareech into a faraway sea. He then killed all the other demons, including Suhavu. The sages blessed the two princes. Thus, Vishwamitra was able to complete the *yajna*.

The next morning, Sage Vishwamitra told Ram and Lakshman, "I want you to come along with me to Mithila."

On the way to Mithila, Vishwamitra imparted immense wisdom to the princes. He also taught them the use of divine weapons.

The three of them came to a dense forest. Vishwamitra warned the princes that a female

demon called Tadaka lived in the forest. She was the mother of Mareech and Suvahu and wanted to kill the princes for killing Suvahu.

Soon they heard a big roar. The sky was pelting stones. Ram and Lakshman aimed their arrows at Tadaka and killed her.

The Four Royal Weddings

As they continued their journey to Mithila, Sage Vishwamitra told Ram and Lakshman the stories of Shiv and Parvati, the birth of Kartikey, the descent of Ganga on the earth and the *samudra manthan*. The princes were fascinated by the stories.

Then Vishwamitra told the princes, "King Janak of Mithila is holding a *swayamvar* for his daughter Sita. Many kings and princes will be present at the *swayamvar*. Sita will choose her husband from them."

In ancient times, the princesses were allowed to choose their husbands. Usually, a contest was held; whoever won the contest could marry the princess.

Lakshman asked Vishwamitra about the contest that King Janak was holding. The sage replied, "Janak has a bow in his palace called the Sunabh, which once belonged to Lord Shiv. The bow is so heavy that no god, *gandharv*, *rakshas* or warrior can lift it

and string it. Surprisingly, Sita had lifted it with one hand when she was just a child. So her father had declared that he would get Sita married to the man who could lift the Sunabh and string it."

The sage and the princes continued walking through the forest. They crossed many streams. At the outskirts of Mithila, they came to an ashram. It was old and no one lived there. Ram asked Vishwamitra, "Why does no one live here?"

Vishwamitra replied, "Once, a sage called Gautam lived here with his beautiful wife, Ahalya. Indra, the King of Gods, liked Ahalya.

"One morning, when Gautam was having bath in the river, Indra disguised himself

as Gautam and entered the ashram. When Gautam saw Indra coming out of his ashram, he became angry and cursed Indra.

"He also cursed his wife Ahalya for not realising that Indra was an imposter and turned her into a stone. Gautam then went away but Ahalya continued to live in the ashram in the form of a stone.

"When Ram accidentally touched the stone in the ashram, Ahalya came back to life. And, as if by magic, Gautam also returned to the ashram. Gautam and Ahalya thanked Ram for removing the curse and started living together in the ashram again."

Vishwamitra and the two princes proceeded to Mithila.

Meanwhile, the news that Ram and Lakshman had slayed Tadaka reached Mithila and spread like wildfire.

The next morning, Princess Sita was returning from the temple when she saw Ram plucking flowers for Vishwamitra's puja. She liked him and hoped he would win the contest and marry her.

Later that day, many kings, princes and mighty warriors assembled at the royal court for the *swayamvar*. A few demons too had disguised themselves as kings and were seated in the hall. One by one, everyone tried to lift the divine bow, but failed. Many of them could not even move the bow.

A few of them lifted the bow but they could not string it. Janak was disappointed. He was worried that nobody would be able to marry Sita.

Finally, Vishwamitra asked Ram to try. When Ram walked up to the bow, everyone in the hall was mesmerised by his grace. He lifted the bow with one hand and strung it easily.

Everyone was stunned. As Ram pulled the string to test the bow, the bow broke into two, with a thunderous sound.

Everyone was shocked. Sita was very happy that it was Ram who had strung the bow. She walked up to him and garlanded him.

King Janak was thrilled. He sent his ministers to Kosal to invite King Dashrath and his family to the wedding. Thus, Ram married Sita.

Ram's three brothers married Sita's three sisters. It was a joyous occasion at Mithila, which celebrated four royal weddings.

Ram Goes into Exile

After the wedding, Dashrath started for Ayodhya with his sons, daughters-in-law and Sage Vishwamitra.

As they walked through the forests beyond Mithila, they were stopped by the angry sage Parasuram. Parasuram hated the

Kshatriyas and vowed to kill them all. As he was very powerful, King Dashrath was nervous.

Parasuram shouted, "Ram! I heard that you have broken Shiv's bow. It was quite old and easily breakable. See if you can string this bow that belonged to Vishnu."

Ram quietly took the bow from Parasuram and strung it with ease. Parasuram was stunned. Ram then aimed at the sage and said, "Sir, I will not kill you. But I will remove your arrogance and the power you have gained in your long life." When Ram shot an arrow, it took away Parasuram's powers.

Parasuram understood that Ram was the incarnation of Lord Vishnu himself. He bowed before Ram and returned to the Himalayas from where he had come.

Dashrath's convoy proceeded to Ayodhya. The entire city was waiting for the newly-wed couples to celebrate. After a few days of celebrations, Bharat and Shatrughan, along with their wives, went to visit Bharat's maternal grandfather.

Meanwhile, Ram and Lakshman helped their father in ruling Kosal. Ram was never harsh on anyone and was always fair to everyone. The people of the kingdom were very happy with Ram.

Dashrath was getting old. So he decided to make Ram the crown prince of Kosal. The priests suggested that Ram's coronation could be held the next day, as it was an auspicious day. Everyone became busy with the preparations.

Queen Kaikeyi had a maid called Manthara. She was an old woman with a hunchback.

Kaikeyi always listened to Manthara's advice. When Manthara heard of the coronation, she ran to Kaikeyi and said, "O Queen, when Bharat is away, the king is planning to hurriedly make Ram the crown prince!"

Kaikeyi was thrilled. "This is good news," she said and gifted Manthara a lovely necklace.

Have you heard the news? Ram will be made the *yuvraj* tomorrow.

Manthara flung the necklace on the ground and said, "How can you be happy? It is not your son who will become the next king. You are Dashrath's favourite queen. Do you remember the two boons that the king gave you long ago? Use them to make your son the crown prince. Ram will not allow Bharat to remain alive if he becomes the king."

Kaikeyi was sure that Ram would never kill his own brother, but the wicked Manthara brainwashed and convinced the queen. Kaikeyi called for Dashrath. When the king entered Kaikeyi's palace, he saw that she was very upset.

Dashrath asked her, "Kaikeyi, what is troubling you?" She replied, "Long ago, when I had saved your life in a battle, you had granted me two boons. Fulfil them now! First, make Bharat the crown prince. Second, send Ram into exile for 14 years!" Dashrath was shocked. He had promised to give Kaikeyi whatever she wished for.

Dashrath pleaded with her, "I will declare Bharat the crown prince, but please do not ask me to send Ram into exile. I cannot live without him." But Kaikeyi said both her wishes had to be fulfilled.

The next morning, when Ram was told of Kaikeyi's wishes, he said, "I will go into exile right away to fulfil my father's promise."

As he prepared to leave, Lakshman heard what had happened. He decided to go along with Ram. Sita too insisted on accompanying them. The three of them left the palace quietly.

The Demons of Chitrakoot

Dashrath's chief minister Sumantra offered a ride to Ram, Sita and Lakshman into the forest. As they left the city, the people of Ayodhya started running behind the chariot. They cried, "Ram, we will not stay in a place where you do not live." Ram asked them to

go back to the city, but they would not. So Ram decided to walk along with the people. Sita and Lakshman also got off the chariot and walked, while Sumantra rode the chariot ahead. After a long time, they reached the banks of the River Tamas. The people who had followed Ram were tired and soon fell asleep.

Ram and Sita made a bed of grass for themselves to rest. Sumantra and Lakshman stayed awake the whole night to keep guard. Ram and Sita woke up well before dawn and silently rode off with Lakshman and Sumantra, leaving behind the sleeping people of Ayodhya. "I hope they go back to Ayodhya now," Ram thought.

Soon the chariot reached the southern end of the Kosal kingdom. Ram thanked Sumantra for the ride and said, "Please return to Ayodhya now. My father and Bharat will need you." Sumantra was sad to leave them, but he obeyed Ram and went back to Ayodhya.

Ram, Sita and Lakshman continued their journey into the forest beyond Kosal. After a while, they reached Shringaverapur on the banks of the River Ganga.

Guha, the king of the forest dwellers at Shringaverapur, welcomed Ram. Guha said, "I heard what happened in Ayodhya. I want

Ram, stay here and rule my country.

to share my kingdom with you. Please take my throne and stay here for 14 years."

Ram thanked Guha. He said, "Guha, you are like a brother to me and I can stay here, but I want to move as far as possible from Ayodhya. If the people of Ayodhya know that I am staying so close to them, they will come looking for me. I do not want that to happen."

That night, while Ram and Sita slept, Lakshman once again stood guard. The next morning, Guha took them across the river in a boat and tearfully bid them goodbye.

Ram, Sita and Lakshman walked for miles for many days through forests, over hills and rocks. They halted now and then to eat fruits and roots or rest under the trees.

Finally, they reached a place called Chitrakoot. It was a beautiful place with majestic mountains and greenery all around. They decided to live there for some time. Lakshman built a beautiful hut on the banks of the River Mandakini. Sita and Ram grew a small garden around the hut. They led a peaceful life.

Meanwhile, when Sumantra reached Ayodhya, he found Dashrath very ill. Dashrath was worried about Ram and asked Sumantra, "Where is my dear Ram? Where have you left Lakshman and Sita?" Sumantra told him where he had left the three of them and that they were proceeding to the Dandak forest. The worried king soon died.

When Bharat and Shatrughan returned to Ayodhya, they were stunned by what had happened.

Bharat was upset with his mother. He knew that Ram was the rightful king and did not want to take his place. So Bharat left immediately to bring back Ram. The queens, ministers and nearly all the people of Ayodhya went along with Bharat all the way to Chitrakoot.

When Ram and Lakshman heard of their father's death, they became sad. Bharat begged Ram to come back to Ayodhya and rule the kingdom. But Ram refused. He persuaded Bharat to rule the kingdom till his exile was over. Bharat returned on the condition that

he would not live like a king in the palace.
He placed Ram's sandals on the throne and
ruled Kosal on Ram's behalf. He gave up his
princely life, dressed in hermit's clothes and
slept on the hard ground in a hut, just like
his brothers Ram and Lakshman.

Jealous Shoorpnakha

After Bharat went back to Kosal, Ram, Lakshman and Sita left Chitrakoot. They went towards the Dandak forest. On their way, they spent some time at the ashram of Maharishi Atri and his wife Anasuya. Mother Anasuya gave Sita divine clothes that would

never become dirty and ornaments that could
never be destroyed.

Ram, Sita and Lakshman thanked the sage
and his wife and went to the Dandak forest.
There were several ashrams in the forest.
The three of them could hear Vedic chants
from the ashrams. The forest air was also
filled with the sounds of birds and animals.

The Dandak forest seemed a peaceful place to live in.

But the sages in the forest told Ram that the forest was not as peaceful as it seemed. Many demons lived there and they ate human beings alive. In fact, the sages were frightened to live in the forest. Ram told them not to worry. "We will protect

This forest is home to many deadly demons.

you and kill all the demons," he said. For the next 10 years, Ram and Lakshman killed many demons in the Dandak forest.

The sages were happy since most of the demons were now dead. Maharishi Agastya was very happy with Ram and Lakshman and thanked them for making the Dandak forest a safe place for the sages to live in.

He told Ram of a place called Panchvati, on the banks of the River Godavari. He said, "You have just one more year of exile and you can spend it there in peace."

Ram, Sita and Lakshman took the sage's advice and proceeded to Panchvati. On the way, they met a huge vulture. The vulture recognised Ram and said, "I am Jatayu, your

I am Jatayu, an old friend of your father.

father's friend." They chatted for a while with the great bird and then proceeded towards Panchvati.

Once again, Lakshman built a beautiful cottage. The three of them lived there happily, dreaming of returning to Ayodhya soon. Ram and Lakshman collected fruits and flowers from the forest during the day. And in the night, Lakshman guarded the cottage. Sita spent her time tending to the garden and playing with deer and rabbits.

One day, while they were sitting outside their cottage, Ravan's sister Shoorpnakha was passing through the forest. She saw Ram and wanted to marry him.

Shoorpnakha used magic and turned into a beautiful woman. She went to Ram and told him that she wanted to marry him. Ram said politely, "I cannot marry you. I am already married to Sita and I have vowed to be loyal to her."

Shoorpnakha insisted, "The woman sitting next to you is very ugly. Leave her and marry me. I will take you to my magnificent palace."

Ram was irritated, but he could not be rude to Shoorpnakha. So he said, "Go to my brother over there. He is handsome and young. He may marry you."

At this, Shoorpnakha felt humiliated. She became angry and said, "This woman Sita is the reason for you not marrying me. I will kill her, and then you will be free to marry me." Shoorpnakha pounced on Sita. But before she could harm Sita, Lakshman ran forward quickly and chopped off Shoorpnakha's nose and ears.

In pain and humiliation, Shoorpnakha ran howling to her stepbrothers Khar and Dooshan. They came immediately to Panchvati with their army and waged a battle. But they were no match for Ram and Lakshman. The demons were soon defeated. Finally, there were no more demons in the Dandak forest.

Shoorpnakha did not fight. She hid herself and watched her brothers getting killed.

But Shoorpnakha still wanted her revenge. So she went to her other brother Ravan, the King of Lanka. "He will definitely help me," she thought.

Ravan and the Golden Deer

Ravan, the king of the demons, was shocked to see his sister Shoorpnakha without ears and nose. "Who did this to you?" he bellowed.

Shoorpnakha lied, "I saw a beautiful woman named Sita. I thought I should bring her to you and make her your wife. When

I tried to do so, her husband Ram and her brother-in-law Lakshman chopped off my nose and ears. They are the same men who killed all the demons in the Dandak forest."

Ravan was furious. He wanted to take revenge on those who had hurt his sister. So he mounted his flying chariot, the Pushpak, and flew to Panchvati. He also took with him the demon Mareech, who could turn into anything at will. Ravan planned to use Mareech to fool the princes and kidnap Sita.

They crossed the sea and came to the mainland of Bharat. When they approached Panchvati, they got off the chariot at a distance from the cottage where Ram, Lakshman and Sita were staying.

Ravan ordered Mareech to take the form of a beautiful golden deer and run towards the cottage. Mareech, now a golden deer, pretended to eat grass. Ram and Sita were sitting under the shade of a tree while Lakshman was fixing the roof of the cottage. They saw the golden deer.

They had never seen such a beautiful creature before. Sita was enamoured by it and longed to have it as a pet. She told Ram, "Please get the deer for me. I would love to take it along with me to Ayodhya."

Ram was suspicious of the deer. After all, no one had ever seen or heard of a golden deer. But Sita was adamant and Ram finally agreed to capture it. Instructing Lakshman to stay with Sita, he left with his bow and arrow, following the golden deer.

Ram found it hard to catch the golden deer, which ran swiftly deep into the forest.

Ram grew more suspicious of the deer. "This is perhaps a demon in disguise and not a real deer," he thought. He decided to shoot the deer rather than catch it alive. So he took aim and shot at the deer.

The arrow pierced Mareech's chest. Mareech knew he would die. So he changed into his real demon form. As a final trick,

Mareech cried out in Ram's voice, as though he was in pain, "Sita! Lakshman! Help! Help!" After this, he fell dead.

Ram was now worried about Sita and Lakshman. "Something is definitely not right," he thought. He ran back to the cottage as fast as he could.

Meanwhile, back at the cottage, Sita and Lakshman heard the cry. Sita began to worry. "Something has happened to your brother. We should go and help him," she said.

Lakshman knew that Ram could never be in trouble. He was strong and fearless. "I know it is not Ram's voice but some demon's.

Lakshman! That is your brother's cry. Go at once and help him!

We must stay right here. We must not fall for the demon's trick," Lakshman told Sita.

Sita became angry. "You know that your brother is in trouble and yet you don't want to help him. You want him to die." Lakshman was shocked to hear Sita speak like this.

He bowed to her and said, "How can you say this to me? You know that I love my brother more than anything else. I want to wait here because Ram asked me to protect you. But now I cannot stay here even for a moment. I will go and come back with Ram."

Before leaving, Lakshman drew a line around the cottage with an arrow. He told

I will go and help Ram, but you have to stay back.

Sita, "You must not cross this line till I come back with Ram. You will be safe as long as you are inside the line."

Lakshman then ran in the direction from which Ram's voice had come.

Ravan Kidnaps Sita

As soon as Lakshman went into the forest, Ravan disguised himself as a sadhu and came to the cottage where Sita was now alone. He cried in a loud voice, "Give me some alms, mother!" As he tried to step over the

line that Lakshman had drawn, huge flames rose from it. Ravan instantly realised that he could not go beyond the line. "I have to make Sita come out and cross the line, otherwise I will not be able to kidnap her," he thought.

When Sita heard a sadhu begging for food, she came out of the cottage with fruits in a basket. She requested the sadhu to come inside. But he refused. He said, "You are insulting me by asking me to come to you for alms. You should come to me!" He pretended to be angry.

Sita did not know what to do. She had promised Lakshman that she would not step over the protective line he had drawn. But

I am a sadhu. I will not come in. You should come out and give me alms.

she also could not let a sadhu walk away in anger. With great hesitation, she crossed the *Lakshman rekha* and went towards Ravan.

Ravan knew he had no time to waste. Ram and Lakshman would return soon. So he grabbed Sita and pushed her into his chariot. He ordered the Pushpak to fly to Lanka. Sita realised that she had been tricked. "I should have listened to Lakshman and not crossed the line. I should not have asked him to go after Ram. I should not have asked Ram for the golden deer," she lamented.

Sita called out to Ram and Lakshman. "Help me! Help me!" she shouted in the direction of the jungle below. Jatayu, the vulture, heard Sita's cries. He immediately

rushed to her rescue. He tried to fight Ravan but he was old and no match for the mighty King of Lanka.

Jatayu fought bravely. He broke Ravan's armour and bow. He even damaged his chariot. Though Ravan was injured slightly, he was stronger than Jatayu. He chopped off

Jatayu's wings with his sword. The vulture fell to the ground.

The Pushpak continued flying to Lanka. Sita threw her ornaments one by one into the forest, leaving a trail for Ram and Lakshman. A few monkeys in the forest found these ornaments.

Meanwhile, Ravan noticed that his sister Shoorpnakha had not lied to him about Sita's beauty. When they reached Lanka, Ravan showed off his rich country and wonderful palaces to Sita. "Marry me and you can rule Lanka along with me," he said. Sita begged Ravan to take her back to Panchvati.

She even threatened him, "Ram will come in search of me and destroy your kingdom!"

But Ravan laughed. "Ram does not know that you are here. I will give you some time to think over my proposal. Change your mind and become my queen," he said.

Ravan left her in the garden called Ashokvan. He ordered many she-demons to guard Sita. He also sought their help in winning over Sita. The she-demons tried their best, but in vain. Sita simply chanted Ram's name over and over again and prayed that she would soon be rescued by him.

Meanwhile, at Panchvati, Lakshman was searching for Ram. Ram was rushing back towards the cottage. He saw Lakshman. On seeing that Lakshman was not with Sita, Ram became worried. Ram and Lakshman hurried to the cottage, fearing the worst for Sita. Their fears were not unfounded. Sita was not in the cottage.

Ram and Lakshman started looking for Sita in the forest. They came across the dying Jatayu. The vulture told the princes that Ravan had carried Sita to Lanka. Jatayu then fell dead in Ram's arms. Ram and Lakshman performed the last rites for the valiant bird.

Ram Becomes Friends with the Vanars

Ram and Lakshman immediately set out to save Sita. But they did not know how to enter Lanka or fight Ravan and his thousands of soldiers to save Sita. On the way, they met an old lady called Shabari. She offered

them fruits and told them to seek the help of the monkey king Sugreev and his *vanar (monkey)* army to rescue Sita. She told the princes, "Sugreev and his followers live on Rishyamook hill."

Ram and Lakshman thanked Shabari for her suggestion and refreshments. They went in search of Sugreev.

Sugreev was sitting on top of the Rishyamook hill. He saw two young men dressed as hermits but carrying bows and arrows. He sent his chief minister Hanuman to find out who they were.

Hanuman went to Ram and Lakshman and asked them who they were.

Lakshman replied, "He is my brother Ram and I am Lakshman, from Ayodhya. We are looking for Sugreev."

Hanuman was excited because he had heard of the princes and how they had slayed the demons of the Dandak forest. He welcomed them and took them to meet Sugreev.

On the way, Hanuman enquired, "Where is your wife Sita? Why is she not with you?"

Ram was quiet. Lakshman explained to Hanuman that Ravan had abducted Sita. He also said that they hoped Sugreev and his monkey army would help them rescue Sita from Lanka.

Hanuman explained to Sugreev why the princes of Ayodhya had come looking for him. Sugreev then took out a bundle and gave it to Ram. He asked, "Are these your wife Sita's ornaments? We found them in the forest." Ram became sadder seeing the ornaments. He said, "Yes, they belong to Sita."

Sugreev then told Ram and Lakshman about his own problems. He said, "My elder brother Bali is the King of Kishkindha. He does not trust me. He thought I was trying to kill him so that I could become the king. He threw me and some of my friends out of Kishkindha and took away my wife Ruma. I will gladly help you rescue Sita with my

I can help you but you will have to help me first.

army but you will have to help me become the king of Kishkindha."

Ram hesitated. He did not want to be a part of the fight between two brothers. But he had no choice. He needed the help of the *vanars*. So he agreed to help Sugreev become the king.

Sugreev warned Ram, "Bali is very strong. He doesn't tire out easily. It will be difficult to defeat him in a fair battle." So they came up with a plan. Ram told Sugreev to challenge Bali to a duel. Now, Bali and Sugreev looked alike. So Ram asked Sugreev to wear a garland of flowers around his neck.

The next day, when Bali and Sugreev were fighting, Ram hid behind a tree and aimed an arrow at Bali.

The moment the arrow struck Bali, he fell to the ground. Bali realised that Sugreev had cheated him. He asked Ram, "I have not harmed you. Then why did you choose to kill me?"

Ram said, "You have been evil in beating your brother and then taking away his wife. You could have forgiven Sugreev, but instead you banished him. It is not a sin to kill a person like you." Bali said, "You are right, Ram. But please take care of my son Angad."

When Bali died, Sugreev and his ministers returned to Kishkindha. The *vanars* of Kishkindha were happy to have Sugreev back. Sugreev told Ram that the entire army was ready to leave immediately to save Sita.

Hanuman Burns Lanka

Hundreds of *vanars* headed south towards Lanka. Ram, Lakshman, Sugreev, Angad and Hanuman were leading them. On the way, Ram, Lakshman and Sugreev planned the attack.

One day, while they were sitting on a mountain, they met a huge army of bears. Jambavan, the leader of the bears, told Ram, "We too want to help you in rescuing your wife." Ram was overjoyed because now they had enough numbers to attack Lanka.

Ram wanted to find out if Sita was really in Lanka before attacking the city. Just then, a huge bird flew towards them. The bird said, "I am Sampati. I overheard someone here say that my brother Jatayu was killed. Is that true?"

Hanuman replied, "Yes. Jatayu was a good friend of Ram's father and he was killed while trying to save Ram's wife." Sampati was saddened by his brother's death. He

looked towards Lanka. Sampati had very good eyesight. He said, "I can see Sita sitting under a tree in Ashokvan."

Ram was relieved. He wanted someone to go to Lanka and let Sita know that they were coming to rescue her. Many *vanars* volunteered to go. But they could not swim all the way. "We can jump," said one of them. "But not all the way," said another. The *vanars* demonstrated how far into the sea they could jump. But none could jump far enough.

Then Jambavan spoke to Hanuman. He said, "You can easily cross the sea to Lanka. When you were a baby, you were blessed by

your father, the wind god. You have great strengths that you are unaware of."

Hanuman was encouraged by Jambavan's words. He badly wanted to help Ram. Hanuman concentrated on the jump. He suddenly grew in size. All the *vanars* were surprised.

Ram told Hanuman, "Give this ring to Sita when you find her. She will recognise it and know that I have sent you."

Hanuman jumped. Everyone watched in awe. He soon crossed the sea and reached Lanka. He searched for Ashokvan and finally located Sita. When the demonesses were not looking, he crept up to Sita and said,

"I am Ram's friend. He will come soon to rescue you." He then showed her Ram's ring as proof. Sita recognised the ring and was thrilled. She gave one of her ornaments to be given to Ram.

Hanuman had an idea. He said, "Mata Sita, let me take you back to Lord Ram. I can easily carry you on my palm." But Sita refused. "No. I want Ram to teach Ravan a lesson and take me back with honour." Hanuman agreed and left the garden.

Hanuman thought, "I will test the strength of the demons. Then I will have more information to give Ram." So he started uprooting the trees in the garden. The demons guarding the place ran after Hanuman. After

doing some more damage, Hanuman allowed himself to be caught.

Hanuman was taken to Ravan. The demon king ordered the monkey's tail to be set on fire. Hanuman was bound with ropes and his tail was lit. Hanuman laughed aloud and shrank in size. The ropes around him loosened and he escaped.

Then Hanuman grew in size. In no time, he burnt down the entire city with his tail. The demons tried their best to catch him but Hanuman was too fast for them.

Hanuman jumped into the sea and put out the fire on his tail. Back home, his friends laughed when he told them what he had

done to Lanka. He then gave Ram a detailed
account of Lanka and the demons in the city.

Ram was pleased. He discussed in detail the
course of action with his army of monkeys.

Building a Bridge to Lanka

Ram had another problem—how would his army cross the vast ocean to reach Lanka? He asked his companions for a solution. Just then, they saw a boat coming towards them. It was Vibheeshan, Ravan's brother. He bowed to Ram and said, "Ravan was wrong

to kidnap your wife. I pleaded with him to return your wife to you and avoid the war. With the war, he would be putting the lives of thousands of demons in danger. But he did not listen to me. So I have come here to be on your side."

At first, Lakshman did not trust Vibheeshan. He thought that Vibheeshan was a spy. But soon he realised that Vibheeshan was indeed there to help them fight Ravan. Vibheeshan told them that the only way to enter Lanka was by building a bridge across the sea.

Ram sat on the seashore and prayed to the sea god for three days. On the fourth day, the sea god appeared before Ram and told him, "There is a *vanar* called Nal in your

army. He is the son of the great architect Vishwakarma. He can build a bridge across the sea."

Under Nal's guidance, the *vanars* helped build the bridge. They brought boulders and inscribed the name 'Sri Ram' on them and threw them into the sea. The boulders floated instead of sinking. A long bridge to Lanka was built. The entire *vanar* army marched on it and reached the shores of Lanka.

Ravan was surprised to see a bridge more than 400 miles long. He wondered how it could be built by monkeys in such a short time. But he was not alarmed. "I have been blessed by Lord Brahma that no

human being would be able to kill me. Ram can never defeat me," he thought. Ravan's uncle Malyavan cautioned him, "You may have been blessed by Lord Brahma. But Ram is the incarnation of Lord Vishnu. He is not an ordinary human being. He may be able to kill you."

While camping on the shores of Lanka, Ram sent Angad to Ravan for a final peace talk. Angad asked Ravan to return Sita to Ram and avoid the war. But Ravan refused. He wanted to go ahead with the war.

The army on both sides blew the conch and the war began. All the *vanars* shouted, "Victory to Ram! Victory to Lakshman!

Victory to Sugreev!" They rushed towards the fortress of Lanka. With the help of trees, rocks and boulders, the *vanars* struck down the towers and gates of the fortress and charged towards the demons inside.

Though the demons had better weapons, the *vanars* fought bravely. In no time, thousands were killed on both sides.

Ravan's son Indrajit was a mighty warrior. Angad fought bravely against him. But Indrajit, using his magic power, became invisible and bound Ram and Lakshman with snakes. The two princes fell to the ground unconscious. Ravan was elated. But Lord Vishnu's vehicle Garud appeared there and ate all the snakes

coiled around Ram and Lakshman. Ram and Lakshman regained consciousness and resumed the fight. The *vanars*, who had lost their spirit when Ram and Lakshman had swooned, regained their enthusiasm and fought bravely once again.

Ravan watched his soldiers fall one by one. Many demons of Ravan's army, including the army chiefs Dhumraksh, Vajra Danshtra, Akampan and Prahast lost their lives in the battle. Ravan finally entered the battlefield when his forces were dying in large numbers. He managed to injure Lakshman, who fell to the ground. Hanuman took Lakshman to a safe place. Ram took over Lakshman's fight. He destroyed Ravan's chariot.

Ravan lost all his weapons. Ram could have easily killed him. But the sun was setting. According to the rules of war, one must not fight after the sun sets. So Ravan was spared. He returned to his palace humiliated.

Ravan Is Killed

Ravan realised that he was losing the battle. So he decided to seek the help of his giant brother Kumbhkarn.

However, Kumbhkarn was cursed to sleep for six months in a year. Ravan sent his men to get him. Several elephants were made

to walk over Kumbhkarn. He still did not wake up. The demons poked him with spears, but to no avail. Finally, after all the failed attempts to wake him up, food did the trick. Kumbhkarn woke up to the smell of food.

After a grand feast, Kumbhkarn set out to meet Ravan. Ravan told him, "Ram has attacked us. I need to win this war at any cost. Go and kill Ram!"

Kumbhkarn rushed to the battleground. He crushed many *vanars* under his feet. But with just one arrow, Ram ended Kumbhkarn's life.

Soon Ravan's brothers and sons were killed in the battle. Ravan lost his courage. Only

his beloved son Indrajit was alive. Ravan was worried for his son's life. But Indrajit continued to fight. He used a Brahmastra and severely injured Lakshman.

Sushen, a *vaidya* (doctor) in the army, saw that Lakshman was dying. He needed some medicinal herbs to save him. He asked Hanuman to get the herbs from the Sanjeevani mountain in the Himalayas. Hanuman flew to the mountain. But he could not identify the herbs. So he brought back the entire mountain. Sushen quickly plucked the herbs and saved Lakshman.

The battle continued. Lakshman resumed his fight with Indrajit. Chanting Ram's name, Lakshman aimed a powerful arrow at Indrajit and killed him. Ravan was shattered.

Thirteen days had passed since the war began. Thousands of demons and *vanars* lay dead on the battlefield.

On the fourteenth day, Ravan came face to face with Ram once again. A fierce battle broke out between them. Ravan used all his powerful weapons, one after another, but Ram destroyed them all with ease. Ram started cutting off the ten heads of Ravan, one by one. But they reappeared. Ram realised it was not going to be easy to destroy Ravan.

Suddenly, Vibheeshan remembered the secret to Ravan's everlasting life. He told Ram, "Ravan has hidden an *amrit* in his navel. Destroy it and he can be easily killed." Ram immediately shot an arrow at Ravan's navel. The *amrit* spilled, and Ravan fell on the ground dead. When the remaining demons saw their king die, they fled from the battlefield.

When Ravan's wife Mandodari heard of her husband's death, she wailed, "I begged him to return Sita to Ram. He did not listen to me. Had he done so, he and all the others would have been alive today." Vibheeshan was pained to see his sister-in-law's misery. He was also sad that he had given away the secret of his brother's immortality.

Meanwhile, Ram searched for Sita in Ashokvan. He was thrilled to see her. However, he told her, "You have to prove your purity by taking the *agni pariksha*." So Sita jumped into a fire. Miraculously, the fire turned into flowers. Thus, Sita passed the test.

Vibheeshan was duly crowned the King of Lanka. After the coronation Ram, Sita,

Lakshman, Hanuman, Sugreev, Jambavan and Vibheeshan flew to Ayodhya in the Pushpak.

The people of Ayodhya were happy to see Ram, Sita and Lakshman return home after 14 years. They welcomed them with flowers and music.

Ram was crowned the King of Ayodhya and Sita became the Queen. Hanuman, Sugreev, Jambavan and Vibheeshan stayed in Ayodhya till Ram's coronation was over. Then they went back to their own kingdoms. King Ram ruled Ayodhya for many years. He was considered the best king ever.

Meanings of Difficult Words

The Princes of Ayodhya

conquer	: take control of a place or people by force
yajna	: a special prayer
prasad	: an offering made to God, often in the form of food
gurukul	: an ancient type of school, in which the students lived with the teacher, often in the same house
guru	: teacher
Vedas and Shastras	: old Hindu texts

Vishwamitra's Request

ashram	: a place where a teacher (guru) lives, prays and teaches
demon	: an evil supernatural being; a devil
hesitate	: to be in two minds before saying or doing something
vast	: huge in size, number or quantity

The Four Royal Weddings

Kartikey	: the son of Shiv and Parvati
samudra manthan	: the churning of the ocean to get nectar
swayamvar	: the practice of choosing a husband from several suitors
gandharv	: a celestial person
imposter	: a person who pretends to be someone else to deceive others
mesmerised	: spellbound

Ram Goes into Exile

exile	: banishment from one's own country
Kshatriyas	: members of the warrior clan
vowed	: made a promise
nervous	: uneasy and slightly scared
incarnation	: God born on earth
yuvraj	: crown prince
coronation	: a ceremony to crown a new prince, king or queen
boons	: wishes; favours

The Demons of Chitrakoot

halted	: stopped
hermit	: a person who has given up worldly things such as beautiful clothes and good food

Jealous Shoorpnakha

divine	: belonging to God
proceed	: to go in a particular direction
humiliated	: insulted
revenge	: the action of hurting or harming someone in return for an injury or wrong suffered at their hands

Ravan and the Golden Deer

bellow	: shout
mount	: get on something to ride it

at will	: at whatever time or in whatever way one pleases to do something
Bharat	: the ancient name of India
adamant	: impossible to persuade; unwilling to change an opinion or decision

Ravan Kidnaps Sita

disguise	: dress up as someone else to hide one's identity
sadhu	: a holy man; hermit
alms	: money or food given to poor people
kidnap	: abduct a person by force
trail	: a mark or a series of signs or objects left by a person, animal or thing
proposal	: suggestion; offer

Ram Becomes Friends with the Vanars

seek	: ask for something
rescue	: save someone from a dangerous or unpleasant situation
duel	: a fight usually using swords between two people to decide an argument

Hanuman Burns Lanka

relieved	: relaxed because something bad has not happened
unaware	: not realising that something exists or is happening; ignorant
awe	: a feeling of great respect and admiration

mata	: mother
bound	: tied tightly
shrank	: became smaller in size

Building a Bridge to Lanka

companion	: person with whom one spends a lot of time; friend
spy	: a person who secretly collects and reports information about the activities of a country or organisation
architect	: a person who plans and builds buildings and other structures
Vishwakarma	: the celestial architect
conch	: a shell that is blown to indicate the start of a war
elated	: extremely happy and excited
Garud	: eagle, Lord Vishnu's vehicle, considered the king of birds
swoon	: faint

Ravan Is Killed

giant	: someone who is extremely tall, big, strong and often evil
poke	: prod
Brahmastra	: Lord Brahma's weapon
amrit	: a divine drink
immortality	: the ability to live forever